Remind Me to Breathe

Erin,

Thanks for all you
do to inspire and
encourage others! ♡

Caro Randall

Remind Me to Breathe

A little book of poems to
help us navigate thoughts
and feelings and return to
the present moment.

by
Lauri Randall

ISBN-13: 978-1-7333439-2-3

"So maybe the key
is to let my thoughts go.
Maybe "I am"
is all I need to know."

~ Remind Me to Breathe

For You

♥

Butterflies

I feel fear of the future
and things I can't plan.
What if's and what could be's,
things I don't understand.

The worries inside me
feel like butterflies
are throwing a party
of stupendous size.

They flit and they flutter
and dance 'round the floor.
They tickle inside me
until I am sore.

I breathe in, count to three,
breathe out counting to four
and slowly the butterflies
leave the dance floor.

I breathe in, count to four,
and breathe out a big sigh
and release all the butterflies
into the sky.

The party is over.
The butterflies gone.
The dance floor is empty
and I'm feeling calm.

Now that I'm no longer
filled up with fear,
I return to this moment
and what's really here.

The things I can touch
and sounds I can hear.
What's real right now,
not what may be next year.

Then I'll take my fears
out from my mind,
and share them all
with somebody kind.

A friend or a teacher
or family at home.
When I share my fears
I know I'm not alone.

Then to all the what if's,
what could's and what might's,
you're not real right now,
so I bid you "Goodnight."

Conversation Starters

The poem mentions butterflies. What does fear feel like in you?

Do you feel different when you're just a little bit nervous instead of anxious or afraid?

Where do you feel fear? Do you notice it in your stomach? Chest? Knees? Toes?

Which is usually true?
1. The things you worry about have already happened.
2. The things you worry about haven't happened yet.

Did you notice that most things we worry about aren't happening right now?

Did you notice that many things we fear might not happen at all?

Can you take three slow, deep breaths to relax your body when you feel nervous or afraid?

Can you notice how your breath feels when you breathe in and out? Is it warm or cool?

Have you ever noticed that many things we fear often do not happen or turn out differently than imagined?

Is fear sometimes fun or exciting like watching scary movies or riding roller coasters?

Notes

Notes

The Vine

When I feel anger,
it grows like a vine.
So hot and red,
it spreads and climbs.

I breathe in, count to three,
breathe out counting to four.
I can feel the vine
drift down to the floor.

I breathe in, count to four,
breathe out counting to five.
I can feel that vine
shrink down to small size.

Now I pick up the vine
and look close to see
who planted a seed
of anger in me?

Was it my best friend
or sister or dad?
Did they hurt my feelings
because they were mad?

Before we decide
who deserves blame
remember, my friend,
that we're all the same.

We all have vines
that grow tall as trees
and make us say things
we don't really mean.

But anger can't grow
as tall as the trees
if we help each other
remember to breathe.

Conversation Starters

The poem mentions a hot, red vine. What does anger feel like in you?

Where do you feel anger in yourself?

Does anger ever involve other emotions like fear or sadness?
If so, how might other feelings be involved?

Is anger usually about things that have already happened?

Does irritation or annoyance feel differently than anger or rage?
How does it feel different?

Is it possible to notice anger when it is just a small seed of irritation
and before it grows into anger or rage?

What are some things you can do so you don't react to your anger
and do or say things you don't mean?

Can you calm yourself by taking several slow, deep breaths?

Can you calm yourself by counting the length of your breaths?
Can you make your exhale one or two counts longer than your inhale?

Can you remove yourself from the situation until you feel calm?

Can you try to understand what happened?

If another person was involved, can you try to understand what emotions they might have been experiencing and why?

Can you use this information to make positive, mindful change if needed?

Have you noticed how your feelings change as you think about things in different ways?

Notes

Notes

Flashlight

Love is a light
in the dark,
like a flashlight
from the heart.

When feelings make
my light grow dim,
aim your flashlight
and look in.

You'll see anger,
fear, and pride.
The parts we sometimes
try to hide.

Love and joy,
you'll see them too.
They're all what make
us, me and you.

If it's just too
dark to see,
please remind me
how to breathe…

soft and deep.
Just talk with me.
Then I'll know you
and you'll know me.

We're not perfect.
That's ok.
We know that we're
enough today.

When we shine flashlights
from the heart
on all our light
and all our dark,

then I'll love me
and you'll love you.
And love can grow
between us too.

Conversation Starters

Think of a person or an animal that you love.

Spend a moment remembering a time you spent doing something nice with that person or animal. You can close your eyes if it helps.

Notice how your heart feels.

Can you describe how it feels?

What would your heart feel like if you thought about a different person or animal?

Isn't it interesting how your feelings might change when you think about different people or animals?

Isn't it wonderful to know that sometimes we can feel love just by closing our eyes and thinking?

Can we feel love for ourselves too?

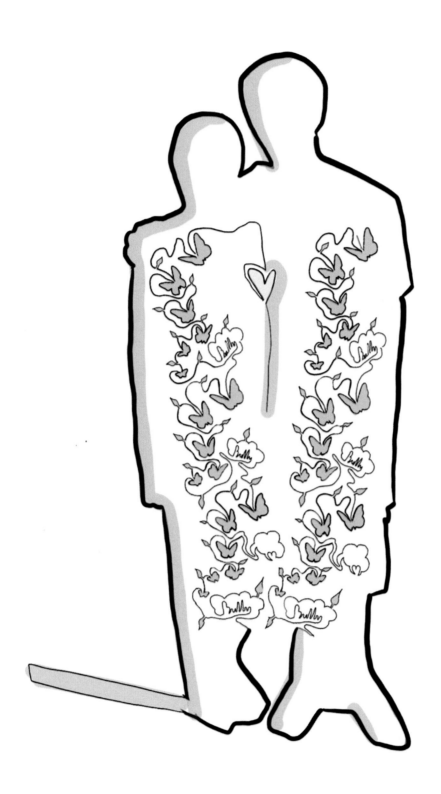

Notes

Notes

Clouds

There's sadness in me.
Reminds me of clouds.
So heavy and dark,
it's weighing me down.

Sadness can be
such a difficult blend
of swirling emotions.
Just wish this would end.

So, please sit with me
just to be there.
Remind me to breathe.
Just listen and care.

I'll let out my tears.
They'll roll down my face.
The clouds will grow lighter
because I am safe.

Safe to feel happy.
Safe to feel mad.
Safe to feel worried.
Safe to feel sad.

See, one feeling's bigger
than all the above.
It's the biggest of all.
The feeling of love.

Every storm passes.
This sadness will too.
And, like falling raindrops,
our tears become fuel.

They water our hearts
and nourish the seeds
of love that is strong
in you and in me.

When this storm has passed
and the clouds have all gone,
we'll feel all the love
that was there all along.

Conversation Starters

The poem mentions clouds.

What does sadness feel like in you?

Where do you feel sadness in yourself?

Do you feel it in your stomach? Your elbows? Your chest?
Your toes?

Do you feel heavier or lighter when you feel sad?

Can it help to share your feelings with someone you trust when you feel
sad?

Does sadness ever involve other feelings like love, anger, or fear?

If so, how might the other feelings be involved?

Can you think of a time that sadness also involved love?

Can you feel that love even when you feel sad?

Do you usually feel sad about things that have happened in the past or things that might happen in the future?

Isn't it nice to know that feelings come and go?

Notes

Notes

i am

I feel joy in me.
It feels so good.
I want it to stay.
I wish that it would.

Feels like bubbles
from bottom to top
floating inside me.
Don't want them to pop.

But then something happens.
Something's gone wrong.
I'm feeling unhappy.
The bubbles are gone.

Someone was hurtful
or maybe unkind.
Now all of the joy
is gone from my mind.

In comes the anger.
Now I feel mad.
Don't know what to do.
No joy to be had.

All of these feelings
they come and they go.
Feels like a whirlwind,
out of control.

I am feeling happy.
I am feeling sad.
I am feeling loving.
I am feeling mad.

"I am" are the two words
that never change,
though my thoughts and feelings
don't stay the same.

So maybe the key
is to let my thoughts go.
Maybe "I am"
is all I need to know.

Conversation Starters

Using the drawing on the next page, complete the sentence "I am ___" with a positive word about yourself.

How do you feel inside when you think this thought?

Using the same drawing, complete the sentence with a negative word.

How do you feel inside?

Did you notice that positive and negative thoughts can feel differently inside of us?

How would it feel if the words we added to the sentence, "I am...," didn't matter?

i am

Notes

Notes

Bully Brain

There's a bully in my brain,
you see.
It makes my thoughts talk
down to me.

It tells me what I
cannot do.
It tells me why I'm
less than you.

It tells me I'm
not smart enough,
or good enough,
or strong enough.

It makes me feel so
bad inside.
It makes me want to
run and hide.

This is when I need
to breathe.
So I remember
I believe…

It doesn't matter whether
I am tall or I am short.
It doesn't matter whether
I am rich or I am poor.

It doesn't matter whether
I am strong or I am smart.
What matters is the love I share
from deep inside my heart.

Conversation Starters

What is a bully?

Bully brain thoughts are unkind thoughts we have about ourselves.

What are one or two unkind thoughts you have about yourself?

How do these thoughts make you feel inside?

Close your eyes and imagine what a caring friend or loving family member would say to you if you shared your bully brain thoughts with them.

How do loving words and thoughts about yourself make you feel inside?

Do this for all of your other bully brain thoughts.

Have you noticed that you feel different when you talk to yourself with kindness and love?

Notes

Notes

Back to Now

Isn't it quite
interesting
the way we're
always thinking things?

Like, "She likes me..."
then we feel glad.
Or, "Why would he...?"
then we feel mad."

Or "What if they...?"
now we're afraid.
Like trees in wind
we seem to sway.

Often thoughts
that make us spin
aren't about
the time we're in.

They're thoughts of future
and the past.
Thoughts of times
beyond our grasp.

But life is here
right now, not then.
So come on back
to now my friend.

See a sight or
hear a sound,
or feel your feet
upon the ground.

Life is here
right now, not then.
So come on back
to now again.

The full-page, single-line illustrations on
the following pages can be tools for
calming a busy mind and returning to
the present moment. Simply
follow each line from beginning
to end. They can also serve
as a gentle reminder that all things are
connected as one.
Enjoy.

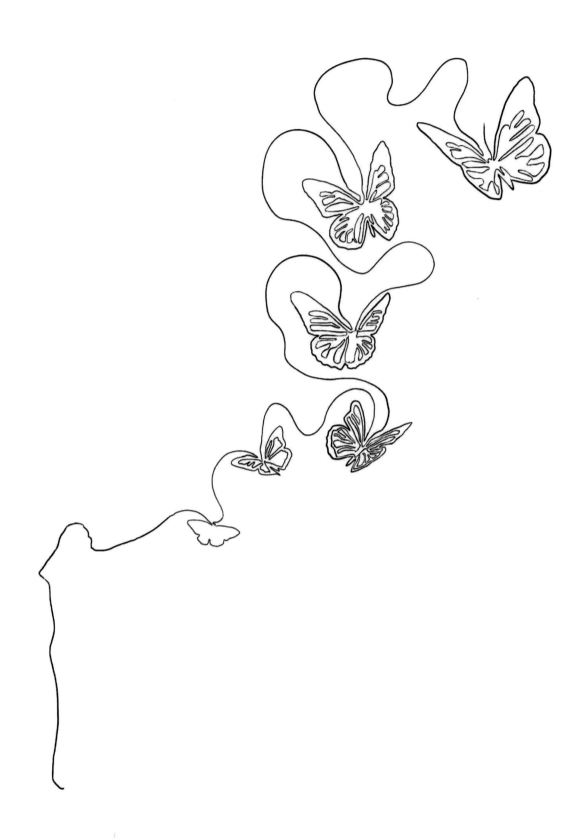

i am

Notes

For more information please visit:
www.remindmetobreathe.com

Thank You.

♥

Made in the USA
Monee, IL
21 May 2020